C000257995

OVER 200 AMAZING
SEX TRICKS
& TECHNIQUES
FOR MEN

OVER 200 AMAZING SEX TRICKS & TECHNIQUES FOR MEN

PHILLIP HODSON AND
ANNE HOOPER

ROBSON
BOOKS

First published in Great Britain in 2001 by Robson
Books, 10 Blenheim Court, Brewery Road,
London N7 9NY

A member of the Chrysalis Group plc

British Library Cataloguing in Publication Data
A catalogue record for this title is available from the
British Library.

ISBN 1 86105 461 0

Printed by Butler & Tanner Ltd, London and Frome
Designed by Richard Mason

Contents

1

A Real Man

Be unashamed

1 Don't feel apologetic for your shape, size or physical appearance.

2 Feel normal even if by some standards YOU THINK YOU ARE NOT. It's the human being inside you that counts.

3 Fetishes: the most well-adjusted male fetishists we know are completely happy with their fetish and open about their interests.

4 This means that it doesn't matter what your lawful sexual interests are – its YOU, your personality, that attracts (or doesn't attract) your woman.

Be supportive to other men

5 Back each other up. If a friend is sexually low try to boost his confidence. Tell him that he is attractive, interesting and has just had bad luck with women. Give him clues about how to get on with women, such as listening and not talking repeatedly about himself.

6 But... don't encourage him to be vulgar. Research shows that although many men are excited by 'filth', women are repelled. The sooner he gets rid of his anger and crudity (which may be compelling him to be gross) the more success he'll have.

Real sex differences

Research shows that there ARE some real sex differences between men and women (although in most respects, the two sexes are astoundingly similar).

7 Men are visual – this means that they are actively turned on by what they SEE. This means that they don't have to deliberately lift a muscle to get an erection – just looking does most of it for them. Be unashamed of your frankly erotic reactions...

8 Men are often fetishists – for reasons as yet unexplained, men, as small boys, appear to be more impressionable than girls. Perhaps it's enough to be intimately handled as babies lying on a rubber mat to establish the foundations of a lifelong rubber fixation? Especially if such an interest is reinforced by constant fantasies during later teenage masturbation.

Unreal sex differences

What you learn is not quite the same as what you innately inherit:

9 Men are more comfortable with their bodies, their genitals and masturbation from a much earlier age than women.

10 This is because men's sexual apparatus is positioned on the body where it can be easily located, even by a child of two. (Actually it is easily located even earlier than that. Studies of baby boys have shown that quite tiny babies discover the joys of genital pleasure.) Boys get tons of practice at sex (with themselves) and gain an advantage over women there. And most societies in history have been less disapproving of their sexual curiosity.

Big penis versus small penis

There have been innumerable surveys of penis size from the famous Kinsey Report to the infamous *Forum* magazine so there is a fair consensus of 'normality'.

11 Eight or more inches is really big but truthfully not better. It may fill up your woman satisfactorily but if she is small built, you are also likely to be crashing into the far end of her cervix and causing serious pain or even womb displacement. Go for the doggy position or ask her to sit on top so she can control the depth of thrust. Remember that the average length of the human vagina is only six inches.

12 Two and a half inches is small but because the owners of these mini crown jewels have to put a little extra into stimulating their woman, they are often the best lovers of the lot.

The average penis

13 The normal range of penis size is from two-and-a-half inches through to ten.

14 Around five and a half to six inches is the American and European average, although please note that penis size depends on the body type you inherit from your native ancestors.

15 In the Far East, for example, where men inherit slim body size, the average can be as much as two inches less.

16 Warning: make sure your condoms fit BEFORE your sex tryst. Even these are sized. In Thailand, where penises aren't as big as those in the West, they only size condoms in superlatives – Jumbo, Colossal and Super-Colossal.

Get the most out of your genitals –
the facts

17 Lubrication inside the penile passage is provided by the Cowper's gland (inside the body)

18 The penis shaft is filled with spongy tissue that fills up with blood during sexual excitement thus producing an erection.

19 The foreskin is the penis's natural protective wrapper.

20 The glans is the head of the penis and exquisitely responsive.

21 The scrotum is a carry case for your balls (testicles) and keeps them at optimum temperature so that your valuable sperm get the best possible chance to score a hit.

22 The perineum is the highly sensitive area. between the back of the scrotum and the anus.

23 The anus is a taboo area because of cleanliness concerns but is densely packed with erogenous feeling.

As hard as humanly possible....

Take *muira puama* – extracted from the Brazilian rain forest tree of the same name. Muira puama appears to increase blood flow in general and penis blood flow in particular. Dr Jacques Waynberg of the Institute of Sexology in Paris says muira puama is one of the best herbs for sustaining optimal sexual performance.

24 One theory has it that muira puama contains a substance (beta sitosterol) that activates the body's receptors for hormones such as testosterone. The better the hormone works within our bodies the higher sex drive and performance we are likely to reach.

An added bonus is that muira puama also guards against rheumatism, which is a double bonus for those wanting to continue their sex life until they drop.

Eat porridge every day

In l986 the Institute for the Advanced Study of Human Sexuality conducted a double blind crossover study of men and women where some were given a wild oats formula to eat.

25 A large portion of men reported increased sex drive, firmer erections and increased sexual pleasure when taking the formula.

26 Women reported increased sexual desire, increased sexual fantasy and more vigorous pursuit of sexual fulfilment.

Theory behind the extraordinary oats? Dr Ted McIlvenna reckons the plant possesses an enzyme that helps unbind testosterone from other substances in the body thus giving the hormone a much greater aphrodisiac effect.

Be a goer – get on the ginseng

A new scientific examination of the fabulously reputed substance ginseng shows it to be an 'adaptogen', which helps you adapt.

27 If you are tired, ginseng will energise you. If you are over-anxious ginseng will calm you down.

28 But ginseng's most famous use is for enhancing sexual response and performance in both men and women.

Chinese tests of ginseng show that it:

29 Increases production of luteinizing hormone which in turn stimulates the production of progesterone.

30 Improves muscle development and increases stamina.

31 Increases testosterone secretion in men and women – testosterone is now believed to be the main hormone responsible for sex drive and performance.

Be a stallion

Sorry guys, this isn't just nagging. If you want to
be the ultimate sex machine with the hardest
cock and the longest performance you need to
back off:

32 Tobacco

33 Alcohol

34 Pot

They really do screw up your sex life. Beer is
particularly bad news for penises (brewer's droop
is real) and the prostate gland. A Hawaiian study
of more than 6,500 men over a period of 17 years
showed that it only takes three bottles of beer a
month for men to develop prostate problems.
This is because the beer increases the levels of a
hormone called prolactin. Prolactin, as well as
triggering prostate problems, is also commonly
associated with flagging sexual interest and
performance. Also: two high-tar cigarettes
smoked one after the other will swiftly reduce
blood-flow into the penis by up to one third.

It's what you do with it that counts

The imaginative lover uses his penis for much more than sexual intercourse. Try thinking of the penis:

35 As a **massage stick** - using a hand to guide it, plus a lot of massage oil, experiment with rolling your penis round your lovers body. The bonus is it feels brilliant for you as well as for her.

36 As a **vibrator** – manipulating your penis with your hand use it to drum against her clitoris – women adore it.

37 As a **sneaky snake** - if your penis has an overpowering inclination to nestle within your woman's crevices, be these the armpit, between the breasts or between the clefts of her buttocks, give in to the innocent wild creature.

Stock up the sperm tanks

If the gypsy in you is longing to spread your seed, you'll be happy to know that there are methods of boosting the powers of the aforesaid seed.

38 Trying eating foods rich in zinc – these include seeds and nuts. Adequate zinc is vital for the production of testosterone, for sperm formation and for prostate health.

39 So knock back a large handful of pumpkin seeds every day!

Custom-flavoured semen

Hoping for a lot of oral sex? Which naturally she will be gasping for? Better aim at improving the smell and taste of your semen as an allurement.

40 Cut down on the pepper and salt – these make semen taste bitter.

41 Go for blander food such as French fries and peas for a 'neutral' odour.

42 Eat cinnamon and sugar for a sweeter tang.

43 Or if she adores a curry, indulge in the new British national dish – chicken tikka marsala – beforehand.

The well-groomed penis

The fashion-conscious penis knows that if it wishes to attract women of superior quality it needs to look good. Good grooming means:

44 Shampoo and set. It's cool to be clean.

45 Hair styling. Using razor and scissors, go for V-shape, heart-shape or inverted pyramid-shape pubes.

46 Smooth to touch – take a tip from African men and oil your wand – experiment with good stuff from The Body Shop, for instance.

Flexi-cock

Want the world's strongest and most flexible penis? Try Kegel exercises (anal-buttock muscle clenches). These consist of:

47 Twitching the penis 10 times a session for at least 3 times a day.

48 Raising your cock by degrees, as if you were erecting it in stages. Try pulling your cock up to 1) a low stage, 2) a medium height and then 3) the summit. Then let it down again in the reverse sequence.

49 Ultimate test. Hang a tea towel on your penis and keep the towel horizontal for five minutes.

To snip or not to snip

A fierce battle has raged, probably since the beginning of time, on the merits of the circumcised versus the uncircumcised penis.

Circumcision – merits

50 Hygiene – prevents inflammation and painful swelling due to infection under the foreskin.

51 Believed to reduce possibility of transmitting sexual disease and of receiving it.

52 If you are a premature ejaculator, circumcision may slow you down – a little.

Circumcision – demerits

53 You will never look the same again

54 You may de-sensitise your penis.

55 It's a painful experience.

56 Cosmetic surgery for re-construction is expensive and isn't very effective.

General view

57 It probably doesn't matter much either way.

Sex Tricks to Tempt and Tantalise Her

2

The all-over body orgasm

The all-over body orgasm

Learn to link her genital excitement with the rest of her skin. Don't make the mistake of thinking her only erotic area lies between the legs. As you stroke and rub her clitoris, always stroke some other part of her body at the same time. You might try connecting the clitoris up with the:

58 Breasts
59 Toes
60 Mouth
61 Anus
62 Armpits

These other areas will get so tuned in to eroticism that they will grow to share it!

Seduction is for the other person

Don't automatically do to your woman what you would like done to you. Her erogenous zones are not yours – they are different. And every person differs from the rest. So think about what would be good for her. If you don't know what this is, try following this suggested sequence:

63   Hug and caress.

64   Kiss first lightly and then passionately.

65   As you undress spend ages cuddling and stroking and hugging close.

66   Only towards the end of this all-over body pleasure, graduate to touching her genitals.

67   Do not go for intercourse without having first stroked her clitoris into excitement.

Enjoy working out your partner's moods

68 If your woman is not ready to get so intimate with you, she will resist. Don't be discouraged if she retreats or pushes you aside. Enjoy the challenge of discovering her way of thinking so that you can assess what feels right (and sexy) to her. Best advice is to make touch gradual, not to rush things. Be prepared sometimes to take days, even weeks, over getting close. Passionate kissing goes a long way to dissolving resistance.

69 Warning: don't confuse her signals of reluctance and inexperience with real signals of not wanting sex. Never force someone or get her drunk or try to take advantage.

Play with her head

Ways of provoking her interest in getting closer to you are:

70 Seeming vulnerable yourself.

71 Being passive and putty in her hands.

72 Being interested in her one day and, when she has clearly responded, playing hard-to-get the next.

73 Being seen to be attractive to other women.

74 Seeming sexually confident (when it's less than true).

Making pretty patterns – with the lubricant

75 When your lover, thanks to your powers of touch, has become a quivering bundle of finely tuned nerves, this is the time to remember the powers of lubrication. If you don't believe there are differences between being touched by a dry hand and being touched by a wet one, experiment on yourself. A wet hand, slipping round your genitals is incredibly sensuous. (It's so sensuous in fact that masturbating with a dry hand is one of the first parts of the exercise to overcome premature ejaculation – on the grounds that you are least likely to let rip at such a time of drought.)

The clitoris –
an exposé

76 The clitoris is a large organ extending either side and beneath the vaginal lips so that most of it tends to be hidden from view. This means that a few women don't even know it is there. Not to mention a lot of men. But this doesn't mean it ISN'T there.

77 The tip can even be hard to find until you learn to recognise its small bud-like shape.

78 This swells on excitement just like a penis does – thought the result is less visible.

79 Once it is seriously excited the tip proves disconcerting because it appears to disappear.

80 You can find it by pulling back the pubic mound with one hand and exposing the flesh.

81 This stretching sensation will also feel extremely erotic to its owner.

82 Very gentle rubbing on an exposed clitoral bud is sensational.

Let your hand feel pleasure

83 If you find manual foreplay boring, tune in to the sensations your own hand is receiving as it carries out its labour of love. All touch can feel erotic and you will find as you vary the pressure you are giving that the variation affects your experience too. The hand is one of the most sensual parts of the human anatomy since it is packed with nerve endings. Touch can make you feel:

✦ Profound friendship
✦ Affection
✦ Sensuality
✦ Eroticism

A limp penis DOESN'T MATTER

Of course a limp penis matters to YOU. But it doesn't matter as much as you think.

84 It is normal for erection to come and go during lengthy lovemaking. Don't think there is something wrong. There isn't.

85 If you are a master of the fingertips, capable of making your partner's body feel on fire, your penis won't matter.

86 If you have real problems with mild impotence, women actually enjoy helping their men to climax.
Women love a challenge!

It's OK to take breaks

87 If sex feels like a major performance, i.e., that you must constantly appear on top of things (especially her), relax. It's OK to take breaks. What's more, it actually gives the two of you time to rest. Sometimes you need this, in order to feel truly open with each other.

Know her excitement

If this sounds over-simple, bear in mind that some men still think a woman is sexually excited when she begins to vaginally lubricate. Real excitement consists of far more. For starters different women need different excitement triggers.

88 A little clitoral massage may do it for one individual.

89 Dirty stories whispered in her ear for a second.

90 General all-over adoration and worship for two days beforehand for a third.

It's your task to find out what suits your woman best.

When she 'goes away'…

91 There comes a stage when your woman looks out of it. She's away in her head somewhere. This can be disconcerting. But don't, whatever you do, try to recapture her attention. When she looks like this it is because she is so focused on the pleasure you are giving her that she has literally entered a different brain state. Far from being distracted, she is paying you the ultimate compliment. She can only get to such a peak of orgasmic balance when she feels incredibly safe and incredibly stimulated. And it is YOU who is doing the stimulating. So feel good – for yourself too.

Best times of the month

Women, being the fascinating and varied creatures that they are, are not always in exactly the same mood every time when it comes to sex. Like men they are subject to the same health problems, stresses and fatigues. Unlike men they are also subject to their monthly hormonal cycle. This means that there are particular days in each menstrual month when they are much sexier than others. The sexier days tend to be in:

92 the five to 10 days following their period

93 the middle of the month, for a couple of days only, when they are ovulating

94 the day (or couple of days) immediately before their period. This is often a dynamite time for lovemaking.

Sex trick: Make a mental note (or even a written one) of your partner's menstrual cycle for a couple of months to gain a good idea of her sexual timing. (For more details see *Over 200 Amazing Tricks and Techniques for Women*)

Best times of the year

95 Studies of men and women affected by SAD (Seasonal Affective Disorder) reveal that there are two peaks for depression brought on by the time of year. Depressive peaks are in winter and (more surprisingly) summer.

This means that if you want to go for the optimal times for amazing sex you should make the most of spring and autumn. Why should this make a difference? Depression is associated with lower levels of the hormone testosterone, and low testosterone is associated with lowered sex drive.

Thumbelina dance

And all the rest of your fingers too. Here's how you perform the Symphony of the Roving Finger and Thumb. Using tons of lube:

96 Stretch your hand across and lightly rub and stroke the insides of her thighs, bring your hands towards her genitals each time and brushing them lightly before going back to the knee again.

97 Brush with your whole hand up across her labia toward the pubic mound. Do not be rough. Make these moves slowly. Deliberately linger.

98 Let one of your fingers (or thumb) 'accidentally' glance inside the labia so that it skims the entrance to the vagina and brushes inside the pubic area, bumping against the clitoris on the way up. Repeat several times.

Go for her clit

99 Focussing your finger more specifically, pull it up against the underside of the clitoral bud and let it bump across the top surface.

100 Using a highly-lubricated forefinger only, delicately saw at one side of the clitoral tip, up and down.

101 Do the same on the other side.

102 Gently rim around the clitoral head with a fingertip (short fingernails only).

103 Gently rim in the opposite direction. These strokes can be done with the main part of the finger held away from the clitoris, then with the main part of the finger right up against the clitoral tip.

104 Circle directly on the clitoral tip, so lightly that you are barely touching.

Go for her G-spot

Your woman's G-spot (if she has one – not every woman does) will be on the upper wall of the vagina, probably a long way back. It helps if you possess long musicians' fingers! The latest theory is that the G-spot is the clitoral root, the very base of the clitoris. Whatever! It feels like a small swelling.

105 To obtain sensual feeling press down on it with the pads of the finger(s), occasionally lightening then strengthening the pressure. The G-spot responds better to steady pressure than it does to rubbing.

Tongue torture - of the most exquisite kind!

106 Always using the tip of the tongue in upward movement, lick from the entrance of the vagina up and over the clitoral tip, repeatedly in short strokes.

107 Try licking first to one side...

108 Then to the other.

109 Then over the top of the clitoris itself.

110 Pointing the tongue, twirl it gently around the clitoris clockwise...

111 Then anti-clockwise.

Further tongue torture

112 Using the tip of the tongue push gently and repeatedly on to one side of the clitoral tip...

113 On to the other...

114 On to the tip.

115 Combine gentle sucking with these strokes.

116 If one or more strokes prove especially effective, stay with these. Once something takes off erotically women prefer repetition until they reach orgasm.

Men's mistakes: the delicate bud of the clitoris is not as robust as the penis. Don't touch it too quickly or too hard. If you touch or suck too hard, she gets de-sensitised – NOT what you want.

3

Sex Tricks to
Tempt and
Tantalise
You

Men's bizarre fantasies

117 The Japanese basket-fuck – this is supposed to have actually happened in bizarre Japanese brothels. One woman is boxed up in a basket that leaves her vagina open to penetration from below. Two other women manoeuvre the basket over their naked client and lower the first woman on to his erect penis. The two women then twizzle the basket so that the first woman spins around and around, giving the man a unique sexual experience.

118 An oriental performer inserts a type of mini wind harp into the woman's vagina and by dint of squeezing and letting go of her vaginal muscles she manages to play a tune. Later the same performer plays a different sort of tune on her client's penis.

Prostitution tricks

International hooker Xaviera Hollander writes that:

119 With very young men she would get them to climax almost immediately by probing their anus with a forefinger. Then she would knead their penis with both hands like a lump of dough until they regained their erection. On this second time they would be less eager to come and in a more controlled state so that this time they were able to pleasure HER.

Moral of this story: either you or your woman friend should keep a fingernail short.

Playing the pink piccolo

Xaviera Hollander wrote of fellatio that her lover preferred her to have a firm grip with her mouth around the upper part of his penis because he experienced less feeling at the bottom of the shaft than he did at the top.

The perfect blow-job has two vitally important mouth strokes, she says.

120 The first is the up and down of the mouth with the lips tightened around the teeth to prevent nipping.

121 The second is the flicking of the tongue, from side to side across the frenulum – the taut string that runs the length of the shaft. It is possible to flicker so fast that the tongue feels like a vibrator.

Stop yourself from coming

You're only a third of the way into glorious sex and suddenly you perceive it is all about to explode – far too soon. Here's what you do:

122 Grasp your penis head around the coronal ridge with finger and thumb and squeeze – HARD. This prevents the ejaculate from leaving the penis and forces your sexual response to go back a step.

123 Or, if you are seriously into fucking, reach round behind you and, grasping your balls, firmly pull down with your hand so that once again you block the tubes.

124 Tao practitioners place a forefinger on a certain spot on the perineum and press firmly to prevent ejaculation. We suggest you practise this one in private first!

Penis bondage

125 If you are into serious restriction you'll like this. You take elastic surgical cord, (emphatically NOT a rubber band that would cut into the flesh) and tie it around the head of the penis while it is still erect. When your mate sucks on you, you will get excited beyond endurance because your penis will literally be unable to go down.

Safety Warning: as with any kind of bondage, NEVER leave your lover (or yourself) tied up for longer than half an hour. Warning signs are when your penis goes purple.

Marshmallow delight

126 Persuade your lovely partner to fill her mouth with marshmallow, which your penis will experience as soft and squashy.

Surgical gloves

127 Or ask her to don a pair of surgical gloves before doing unspeakable things to your genitals by way of 'medical' examination.

Health charm

In case there are any men out there who still believe it is unhealthy to masturbate, please be aware that some doctors think:

128 Regular masturbation drains the body of seminal fluid thereby helping the individual avoid congestive prostatitis.

129 If the penis is not 'used' regularly (so that it 'remembers' how to get excited, get erect and retain erection) the erection mechanism might get 'rusty' and, at a later date, find it difficult to start again.

Fuck the world

130 Most unusual masturbation story is that of a teenager heavily warned against masturbation by super-zealous parents. The only way he could get away with the act and conceal the evidence was to take the old schoolroom globe of the world, make a smallish hole at the South Pole, stuff this with tissues and then literally fuck the world.

World records

131 The Kinsey Report described one individual who masturbated twenty-three times a week. Amazingly enough he still retained his hearing, his eyesight and he did not succumb regularly to the flu.

132 Viva, the US supermodel, described in her autobiography how she and her lover set out to break the world record for orgasms. She found after two and a half days in bed, that she literally could not continue. Her body seemed to have gone on strike.

133 Kinsey also recorded the case of one man who had three orgasms a day over a period of 30 years and another who averaged 33.1 orgasms a week over a 30-year period. However, Kinsey also found that the younger you were the more likely you were to experience successive orgasms.

The rubber follies

134 Put a large rubber sheet down across the floor. Coat yourself and your partner liberally with massage oil and then conduct a wrestling match in the nude. First one to achieve three holds can ask for any sexual service they want.

135 **Sex trick**: coat the rubber sheet with oil too for more spectacular slippage.

Aides
spectaculaires

If oil doesn't do it for you, some of the newer sex lubricants may. There is:

136 Sylk. Tasteless, odourless and non-greasy, Sylk mimics the natural vaginal juices. A free sachet is available for sampling. Especially important, Sylk is safe to be used with condoms.

137 Platinum Wet. This is a top quality US lubricant made by Dr Johnson. It comes in a sexy black bottle and stays wetter and slipperier for longer than any other lubricant in clinical trials. For use by men and women, it's oil free and may be used with condoms.

138 Spike - anal lubrication. Also by Dr Johnson, this comes in a concertina shaped squeeze bottle with a long probe applicator for delivering deep inside.

139 All these lubricants can be bought from Passion8. For address see page 133.

Perfect place for a little out of body experience

Sexiest choices for the most exciting place in which to have oral sex or mutual masturbation include:

140 Under the blanket on your plane trip.

141 In the toilet during your train ride.

142 In the back of your car, while parked in the local beauty spot.

143 In the stationary cupboard.

144 On the kitchen table.

145 À la Richard Gere – on a grand piano.

Serious warning: it is (often) illegal to have sex in public places so please be exceedingly careful or wait till you get home.

Putting off the heavenly moment

Many people believe that you experience orgasm much more profoundly if you forgo having an orgasm on at least two out of three lovemaking episodes.

146 Mentally you are said to desire sex much more strongly.

147 Emotionally, when orgasm does arrive you are more likely to be deeply moved.

148 Physically, the final release will be cataclysmic by comparison with routine climax.

At least, that's the PR version. Not one for impatient lovers.

Things your woman can do for you

If you ask her nicely!

149 Fill her mouth with toothpaste as she gives you fellatio. Or brandy.

150 Suck on a strong mint while doing likewise.

151 Place her finger and thumb in a ring to her mouth and then use the ring as an outer part of her mouth while she gives you oral sex. The advantage is that she can contract her digits to give you a tighter fit.

152 Use her free hand to stroke as many parts of you as she can find while having intercourse. She might aim at: the thighs, the buttocks, underneath the testicles, twirling your nipples or into the anus.

Rear window

Provided your woman gives you her complete agreement, go for anal sex. Best ways to do this are:

153 To lubricate your penis and her anus liberally.

154 To work on widening her anus with your forefinger. When you can get so that you can fit at least two fingers into it, this is the time to slip your penis in.

155 If she goes into spasm, just wait, moving only enough to keep your erection.

156 It takes time to stretch open enough to let the experience become painless. Do not rush things.

Prolonging your orgasm

You might:

157 Withdraw from intercourse just before the point of no return, only going back to it a little later.

158 Go into slow motion mode just before ejaculation. Slow all body movements.

159 Some people use sexual leisure drugs such as butyl or amyl nitrite ('poppers') causing the reduction of total blood pressure and serving to prolong and delay the experience of orgasm in both sexes.

Warning: little pharmacological testing has been done on these products. Doctors state people with heart or circulatory disorders should not use them. Do not combine the use of these poppers with Viagra or you can suffer from such catastrophically low blood pressure that your heart could stop.

160 Restrain the testicles by hand – holding them away from the body.

All-time favourite erotic treats

161 Provoke a quickie. You strip naked – she remains clothed.

162 Get her to leave her panties on during sex.

163 Challenge her to make you hard without touching your penis at all. A clue. If she mouths the words 'I want you inside me please' but doesn't come near you, you'll find that helps!

164 When she has removed her bra take her head in your hands and place her ear right over your heart so that she can hear its beat and listen to your desire.

More erotic treats

165 Ask her to gently pinch your nipples, trying out softer and harder clamps. Give her feedback on how hard you would really like it. And then get her to do it like you say.

166 Ask her to wedge her vibrator in between you as you have intercourse. Then use it to make her come while you are still inside her.

167 Suggest she puts lipstick around the head of your penis and next sucks it off.

168 Ask her to take her clothes off and sit on a chair at the opposite side of the room. Next ask her to masturbate, promising her that you will not move from where you are seated. Then honour the promise.

4

Porn, Pix,
Sex Toys
and the
Internet

Vibes - the very latest models

There's a small revolution going on in the sex toys industry. Vibrators are being transformed as a result of the fabulous new materials now available. They are soft, malleable, feel like real skin in fun materials such as see-through translucent jellies and gorgeous jewel-like in colour. Here are some of the best taken from the top vibrator website on the Internet, www.goodvibes.com

Vibes for you

169 Cyberskin Vibro Sleeve. A stretchable sleeve made of cyberskin that fits over the penis and includes a vibrating egg for stimulating the sensitive head of the penis.

170 Ball stretcher. A comfortable strap that wraps around the top of the scrotum and is then tightened. The 8 oz weighted bag attached to the strap pulls down the testicles making for surprisingly prolonged sensation.

More vibes for you

171 Neptune ring vibe. This is a tiny vibrating dolphin attached to a cock ring. This works either by giving your lover a solo buzz or by stimulating the clitoris during intercourse.

172 Gummy Bear ring. A jelly rubber cock ring that fixes at the base of the penis (or dildo). The blue model comes with a mini-probe for focusing on the G-spot and the red model comes with little side flaps that tickle the clitoris.

173 Kiwi Ring vibrator. This is a lavender cock ring with a kiwi beak at the tip that pecks at your lady's clitoris. It is powered by a silver bullet-shaped battery (that fits in to the base of the ring), which is so forceful that it practically drills.

Vibes for both of you

174 The Hitachi Magic Wand is still the Rolls Royce of vibrators. This enormous two-speed mains-operated model possesses a sturdy wand handle and a huge vibrating head. What is new about it is that there are now attachments fitting onto the head that focus on clitoral stimulation.

175 Dr Scholl's Deluxe Wand. Dr Scholl has graduated from sandals and is now selling his own version of the Magic Wand.

176 Attachments. What is special about the last two vibrators is that there are some cute pink or purple G-spot attachments that can also be used to give you a prostate massage. Plus one has a slender curved tip specially shaped to give maximum pressure on the front wall of the vagina where your woman's mysterious G-spot is located.

Pulsating Vibrators. The very latest models don't just vibrate. They do a lot more besides. The key difference is:

They pulsate, which your woman might recognise as integral to her style of orgasm, especially for G-spot stimulation.

They are a lot quieter so you can let rip without telling the entire household.

177 **The Pulsatron** has seven different speeds, throbs and pulses.

178 **The iSurge Vibe** has five variations, which include vibration, pulsation, escalation and roller-coaster.

Glow in the dark

179 Pretty in Pink is phallic shaped but consists of a series of graduated beads, the largest at the bottom tapering off to the smallest. Made of pink jelly rubber, it is soft. And firm. And very quiet.

180 Pretty Kitty is a silicone vibrator shaped like a kitten which when used upside down vibrates the clitoris while probing (with Kitty's tail) the vagina or the anus. Nicely quiet.

181 Flex-o-Pleasure consists of a slim handle, a long thin shaft headed by an angled vibrating head. If you like extra stimulation during intercourse this is the perfect one.

Finger vibration

182 Fukuoku 9000 is one of the most ingenious newer vibrators. Devastating in company. Working off tiny watch batteries it fits over your finger like a tiny finger sheath and vibrates. There is no battery pack and no cord. Brilliant for surprises during intercourse since it is virtually undetectable. The kit includes textured rubber pads to fit over the device so that you vary your finger sensation.

183 Pocket rocket is a small rocket shaped vibrator – a little like a pocket torch in appearance. But what transforms it are the wonderful jelly rubber sleeves that fit over it. Comes in lustrous almost edible colours such as blueberry, grape, lime, strawberry and tangerine. You can also add jelly rubber sleeves shaped like a bunny (with extra long ears!) or a variety of nubbly textures.

All these vibrators can be obtained from www.goodvibes.com, but if you prefer to buy in the UK see page 133 for details.

Anal creations

184 Thai beads. A string of three small pearly-pink beads to be inserted into the anus and then pulled out slowly, either to accentuate stimulation or in a rush, to heighten climax.

185 Jumbo beads. A graduated larger version.

186 Jelly beads. Spongy ruby-coloured equally sized jelly beads with a ring pull that offers a firm jelly-like sensation.

Butt plugs

Butt plugs are designed to be worn for the feeling of fullness. They are made in silicone or rubber and are easy to clean. Sh!'s butt plugs come with heart-shaped bases and the silicone is excellent for transmitting vibrations – all you have to do is apply a vibrator to the base. These plugs come in a variety of shapes and sizes. There is:

187 The long thin pointed plug.

188 The shorter, fatter, slightly curved version.

189 The small, squat, fat beaded version.

Hands free

190 **The double delight.** A variety of two-ended dildos to be worn by heterosexuals when the man enjoys anal penetration.

191 **The mini-hummer** offers targeted vibration for women who find it hard to come. She wears it strapped into place over the clitoris, held on by an elastic waist strap and leg straps. Brilliant during intercourse because it sets you going too.

192 **Triple Stimulation.** This is a cock-ring with a flexible dildo for anal penetration while you penetrate her vagina in the time-honoured manner.

All these anal products can be viewed on
www.sh-womenstores.com

Fun lubes

Lubricants come in dozens of flavours and colours. Try:

193 **Edible lubes**, small gelatine filled capsules that you bite on during oral sex to flood your partner's genitals with sweet-smelling edible gel.

194 Or chocolate-flavoured **gel**.

195 Or a row of little **gelatine pots** for flexibility of selection.

There are so many different sorts that you are best advised to search two main sites for suggestions. Go to www.annsummers.com or www.goodvibes.com You can use lubes to spice up the greatest cunnilingus of your woman's life.

The goody bag

196 The goody bag

These days it's getting positively normal to spice up the bedroom with toys. Ann Summers, the British high-street sex shop chain suggests:

✦ Hand cuffs, in black leather or pink and fluffy
✦ Self-adhesive diamante tattoos
✦ PVC blindfold
✦ Kinky heart-shaped bottom paddle
✦ Fur collar and lead
✦ Nipple chain.

Restrain yourself please

Several US erotica companies revealed that nipple clamps were at the top of the best-selling lists last year. Addresses on page 133.

197 Favourite restraint equipment includes:
+ whips
+ canes
+ paddles
+ cat o' nine tails
+ tackle for tying your partner to the bed, or padlocking her to the furniture.

Something for Sir

Skin Two (address on page 133) makes exceptional clothes out of rubber and PVC. They are slick, shiny and skin-tight. They are also beautifully cut, immensely flattering and stunningly erotic. In fact they are works of art. The PVC comes in several new textures. As well as the original PVC there is a realistic leather look, a matt version like unpolished rubber, snakeskin and a slinky sensational satin finish. The clothes include:

198 Glossy rubber underwear in cherry red and black;

199 Shiny white rubber skin-tight fitting jodpurs with tall black shiny boots.

200 Brilliant blue tight briefs with a thong that disappears between your buttocks.

201 Pièce de resistance – a shiny black skin-tight PVC catsuit with a double zip from the front of the neck through the crotch to the base of the spine.

Sexual electricity

There's the emotional electricity that sparks between you and your woman. But there's also the sort that uses Faraday electricity and bombards her with safe, low voltage, mini-lightning bolts. Many of you will have heard of TENS machines, small box-like objects used in physiotherapy, which, by pulsating a tiny electrical charge into the skin, relieve physical pain.

202 Now there is a sexual version of a TENS machine called The Violet Wand. It's been on sale since the 1930s and is presently enjoying a resurrection of interest. It operates by sending sparks through a single electrode and creates an incredible array of sensations. When held near your body it sends out a continuous stream of tiny lightning bolts, and gives off a distinct purple light. Try kissing while plugged in – better than any spark from a hotel carpet!

Available from:

www.stockroom.com/sec0506.htm are several sex toys (including The Violet Wand) that use the Faraday principle. There are electrical:

203 Butt plugs
204 Cock rings
205 Vaginal shields

There is also a book entitled A Guide to Electrical Sex, which is the first of its kind to explain the Faraday sex phenomenon.

Safety first – The Rules

✦ Never do anything to anyone against his/her will.
✦ If you are in doubt, ask or don't do it.
✦ When playing games of restraint devise a safety word, which will be strictly adhered to.
✦ If instinctively you do not trust someone enough to want to play sex games, respect your inner judgment and suggest instead that you and your friend spend more time getting to know each other.
✦ Ask about AIDS exposure.
✦ Practise safer sex (see pages 127)
✦ Do not do anything that would harm anyone.
✦ Practise birth control

Sex as art

At the times when we are not actually having sex many of us like to think about it or even to view it.

206 If you want to look at the sumptuous work of illustrator Vargas you can see it by going to www.eroticart.com

207 Famous US sex educator Betty Dodson wears another hat as a powerful illustrator of erotic subject matter. Her Leda and the Swan is to die for. Go to www.bettydodson.com

Send your loved one a card

Only make sure this is the kind of card to surprise and titillate. Options to choose from on www.kinkycards.com are:

208 Old-fashioned Edwardian pin-up pix.
209 Strange airy fairy draperies from the 1970s.
210 Very up-to-date kinky humour.

Warning: don't forget, it's an offence to send anything deemed obscene through the post.

An erotic review

For a particularly British way of viewing sex take a look at www.eps.org.uk EPS stands for Erotic Print Society and their unique site displays and sells

211 Art books.

212 Limited editions.

213 Portfolios.

214 Photography.

215 Prints.

216 Best of all is the *Erotic Review*.

The latter combines a wicked sense of humour with some of the best English public school predilections for spanking, caning, bare bottoms plus good writing. Personal favourite: Sylvie Jones – 'A Wicked Pack' – playing cards as you've never seen them before.

Sextremes

Wonderful Strokes for Folks

Breast strokes for folks

Offer warm sensual caresses on all parts of your woman's body. Include the breasts in unhurried fashion. Once she is relaxed coat your warm hands with massage oil and begin.

217 The Diagonals. Place your left hand just below and to the left of her left breast, palm downward, your fingers pointing towards her right shoulder. Slowly and without pressure slide the flat of your hand up and over the left breast diagonally off towards the right shoulder. Before your left hand ends the stroke, start another in the same place with the right hand. Then do the same for the opposite diagonal.

218 The Spirals. Coat a warm fingertip lightly with oil (and with fingernail well trimmed) gently and slowly circle the outside of her breast. On completing each lap, slightly shorten the circle a little so that your finger is effectively climbing a spiral around her breast with the aim of ending at a tiny fixed point on the nipple, having circled it several times first.

Sex trick: experiment with different speed and pressures and don't be afraid to ask which feels best.

219 The crab. With hands bunched in crab-like shapes, place them on one of her breasts, fingertips only, either side of her nipple, and very slowly draw the hands apart and down the sides of the breast. Repeat for the other breast.

Sex trick: Don't forget to stroke your partner on every part of her body at every opportunity.

220 The seashore. With both hands bunched in crab-like shapes, place them on one breast, fingertips only, either side of her nipples and draw them down in opposite directions until they end diagonally apart, then draw them together again up and diagonally in the opposite direction. This constant together-then-apart motion is intended to feel like the tide going in and out at the seashore.

221 Raspberry nipple. Tell her you're got her favourite flavoured ice cream on hand and want to feed it to her spoonful by spoonful. What you don't say is that you are a messy boy and will be spilling the occasional dollop en route. Target her nipples. The spillages will need retrieving probably by tongue. Since yours is the nearest one available it is your clear duty to use it.

Sex trick: Make sure you swirl the ice cream all the way around both nipples, a lot.

Tongue twisters. Want to give your woman the most amazing oral sex ever? The secret is to exercise your organ of exquisite pleasure by practising the following exercises in front of the bathroom mirror at least twice a day for a fortnight.

222 Pointing your tongue and pushing it forward a little, flicker it from side to side, keeping up a steady rhythm.

223 Still pointing, flicker it up and down, keeping up a steady rhythm.

224 With a broad tongue, practise lapping, with the focus on the upward movement of the tongue, therefore providing an upward beat.

Lip synching... Here's where you match your well-tempered tongue to your lover's longing skin.

225 Daisy kisses. Plant small kisses, which contain just a little suction from your lips, all over your partner's body, including behind her and finishing off on the labia.

226 Ice cream lick. Treat your partner's genitals like a giant ice cream and, using the broad blade of your tongue, lick her in luscious strokes.

227 The lipstick. Moistening part of her body and lavishly moistening your own lips, slide your lips gently backwards and forwards over the area as if you are applying lipstick.

228 Snake Tongue. This is where your tongue twisters come in useful. Rapidly flicker the tip of your tongue across her flesh.

Sex trick: Work your way up her labia, ending up by flickering across the head of the clitoris.

229 School of Sucking. Gently slide your lips, sucking on pathways along your parner's body. Gliding up the inner thigh can be effective because you meet her genitals at the top. You might try gently at each of her labia. Then slide up to her clitoris and suck on it. You might repeat the exercise, with the further option of flickering your tongue at the same time. Keep moistening your lips.

These tongue strokes are inspired by Ray Stubbs, guru of all types of sensual massage. See the appendix for details of Ray's book.

230 In and Out Suction. Suck a nipple, or an earlobe or her clitoris gently into your mouth. Then, while maintaining the suction, push with your tongue so that you are partially but not completely expelling the organ. Then draw the organ back in again. You can practise on your own fingertip to work out the best methods.

Sex trick: if you do this with an earlobe, be careful not to make sounds that will blast your loved one's eardrum.

The sexiest positions are not the ones where you swing from a chandelier. Surprisingly instead they are the tried and true moves but with a few added extras to streamline.

231 Sex from the rear with fingers. There's something about sex from the rear that sends the senses of men and women galloping. Perhaps it's because we find ourselves pitchforked back to caveman behaviour but the sight of those rounded moons penetrated by your dancing stick says it all.

Sex trick: add your fingers to your partner's clitoris while you take her from behind.

232 The Missionary Plus. Do you know why the Missionary position became an all time favourite? The answer: it works so well on a lot of levels. It allows face-to-face contact, which means we can look each other erotically in the eye. It provides skin-to-skin full frontal contact, which is incredibly arousing and even if female climax is a bit hit and miss, it works a lot better orgasmically than say sex from the rear.

Sex trick: add your fingers or one of these new slender vibrating probes to the act so that her clitoris gets the attention it deserves, which sadly intercourse alone does not provide.

233 Double dildo. Want to do something a bit different in bed? A little out of the ordinary? Take a tip from your lesbian friend and invest in a double dildo. What can a heterosexual couple do with one of these? Elementary, my dear Watson. You can insert it into her, while she inserts it into you...! If she then gently moves it inside you, you will find your own G-spot massaged (in the male's case this is the prostate gland) and believe us, you won't be able to control yourself.

Stop gaps. Some seriously sexy woman adore anal stimulation. Some enjoy as many fingers as you care to insert. But most of us are so influenced by rigorous cleanliness training as children we find it hard to believe that anal play might be acceptable. So we don't make the special moves that many women would welcome. Yet there are ways now of introducing anal play as part of the heterosexual experience.

234 Try using a butt plug prior to/during intercourse next time the two of you get together. Sh! sell these in graduated sizes (see page 133) and shapes. If you or your woman is anxious about first time usage, invest in the smallest size, which will be the easiest to insert. Some also vibrate.

Sex trick: don't surprise your woman with this. Please be certain she will welcome the notion otherwise your move might feel like assault, which would definitely not be a good idea. Note: trim all fingernails or use surgical gloves and loads of lubes for any serious anal handwork.

Private film show. Turn the bedroom into a small cinema. Equip the room with low lighting, a TV screen, a box of chocs and a steamy sex film. I'm not talking the rather crude blue sort here. These do turn guys on but... if they are too crude they turn women right off. This is not what you are aiming at. So see if the video shop has in store:

235 *Nine and a half weeks*

236 *Ai no corrida*

237 *The Kama Sutra*

Pushing it further. Always secretly wanted to be a stud? We have ways of helping you do this...! You might consider, on an occasional basis, using:

238 Viagra. Not for those with any inkling of a heart problem but this can and is used by men who do not have impotence problems but who simply want an erection that persists. If you can't get a prescription from your doctor, you certainly can buy it through the Internet. Just type in the name on your favourite search engine.

239 Viacreme. This is the new L-arginine cream that you rub on to your penis (woman can use it on the clitoris too). It tingles, drawing the blood to your delicate organ and giving you a stiffie. (See the Internet for more details). The Romans used stinging nettles!

Pushing it even further

240 Testosterone for men. Comes in a tube of cream or gel, you rub it into the skin, and feel like a teenager again. Offers extra sex drive, arousal, sensitivity, stronger orgasm.

241 Testosterone for women. Also comes in a tube in gel form, but of a much lower strength than that for men. With very similar results.

242 Vasofem. This contains phentolamine which helps women overcome arousal difficulties. It's still being researched and in spite of a scare with the laboratory rats, it is looking extremely promising.

Future aphrodisiac. So what are the future attractions in the shape of orgasm inducers?

243 The new Eros-CTD looks like an oxygen mask but this one is fitted over the clitoris and thanks to super-batteries, it provides a gentle suction to stimulate blood flow. It does give women orgasms and works so well that the women in the original study refused to give the little pumps back to the clinical company when the study was finished.

244 Remote control sexual reflex trigger. Testing is underway for a remote controlled device that is surgically connected into the nerves of the spinal cord that trigger orgasm. Could transform the lives of people with spinal disability.

6

Sexopoly –
Games that
Lovers Play

Rules of gaming

245 Do not play any sex games with someone you distrust or someone you have only just met.

246 Both of you must be willing. It is out of the question to force games on someone who, say, has claustrophobia. Or indeed to force games on anyone.

247 Agree an emergency word or phrase, which is your safety code, which you KNOW will always be respected.

248 Do not attempt any games with someone in poor health.

249 Do not restrict airways or use tight restraints that prevent proper circulation.

Gaming props

250 Be subtle. Start light bondage games by using simple items such as a silk scarf, tights or a tie.

251 Buy a sleep blindfold. It can be used for having a quiet night and then for having a really exciting one.

252 Squares of silk, satin and fur are amazing secret weapons

253 Top up with warm massage oil and possibly with ice-cubes!

Judging your partner's mood correctly

As you can probably imagine, it might be disastrous to advance upon your lover with a silken rope only to discover that she can't even cope with oral sex, let alone anything more daring.

254 Get to know your partner well. Talk about how far each of you would like to go. Surprisingly this is easier done at the start of a relationship.

Sex trick: talking about your desires to get into gaming can be an erotic build up in itself, provided your partner is like-minded.

Provoking and tantalising

255 As you stroke and caress (as you would at the start of any lovemaking of course), build a picture in words of how you most enjoy touching and stroking her most secret recesses but don't exactly match the words with actions. Stroke near but not on the places she most wants you to touch. The key to success is 'frustration of expectation'.

Sex trick: get her used to you not touching her most sensitive zones then accidentally let one finger wander and trail ever so lightly across the genitals. If you are doing it properly, she should gasp.

Raising the temperature

256 Now you want to suggest to your partner that it's time for a little extra surrender: 'Would you like to feel unlimited pleasure, to go almost crazy with desire?' you might enquire. 'You would? Then keep your hands over your head while I get to work.'

The takeover

257 It's very difficult to keep your hands over your head while being teased just off centre below the waist, so your lover is likely to disobey. Now you suggest a little help in keeping her hands out of the way: 'Let me just bind your hands together with this silk scarf.'

Sex trick: on this first occasion remember – less is more.

As you tie the knots you might whisper: 'Relax. Forget the day, forget where you are, lose yourself, don't think about me, let your mind wander where it will and visit that secret erotic place only you know about and can enter.' All the while make your caresses more persistent and feather-light.

The blindfold

258 Hint in a subdued voice how it might be fun for your partner to close her eyes, to see nothing, to float into darkness and focus on her dreams, and suggest she could find this easier if she borrowed your bedside blindfold.

Be cautious

259 Be loving and do not rush things. Be ready to switch back into a more conventional mood the minute your partner indicates she wants this. The entire success of this sort of game depends on the rapport that the two of you strike up. You must tune in to her mood for games of restraint and domination to work. If she goes cold on you, stop immediately. It means she is scared.

But once the two of you have agreed, what are the blindfold games you might enjoy?

Forfeits. This could consist of caressing your woman and forbidding her to utter any sounds of appreciation. If she forgets, she has to tolerate:

260 A mild spanking.

261 An ice cube pressed to the navel.

262 Her nipples tweaked.

Sex trick: the secret here is to pretend she has erred even when she has not.

263 In the red museum. You are an exhibit and your dream partner is blindfolded. She has to identify you through caressing your naked body and you cannot move, regardless of where she touches.

264 The rape of the seven veils. A beautiful slave is brought to the auction block swathed in cloaks and scarves. The cruel slave master slowly peels these away as he describes exactly what he plans to do to the slave. Beneath the cloaks are many thin veils. For each veil that is ripped off, the slave is ravished in some terrible manner.

265 The high-class hooker. Your partner is a high-class hooker. You, as her client must tell her exactly what you want her to do. Every time she finishes one activity she must ask for the next command. You continue until one of you can go no further.

266 Torture by tickling. Literally what it sounds like. Bind your partner (loosely) to a bed then target her most sensitive areas. Ensure that your touch is extremely light and moves rapidly like a spider darting.

Most ticklish areas: feet, belly, armpits, inner thighs, around the breasts.

267 Play at pornographers. If you have your own video camera and PC editing suite, make your own 'blue' movie. Then watch it together from your bed. A word of warning. If there is any likelihood your partner is not trustworthy, don't do it. Intimate pictures have been known to show up on people's computers on the other side of the world.

268 Sitting in the backseat. Drive out to a secluded place where you cannot be overlooked and move to the back seat. In spite of the inconvenience and the cramps the sheer unfamiliarity of the surroundings gets you moving at up to 100 mph.

Want to feel different?

269 It sounds crazy but try doing something quite bizarre. For example, put on tight-fitting rubber underwear one day before you go in to work. Or snap into a pair of your woman's panties underneath your office suit. The constant awareness of your body and its reactions to the unfamiliar materials can be extremely sensual. Not to mention the overpowering desire to confide in a female colleague about your sensual undies.

Want to look different?

270 If you've been dying to experiment with cross-dressing but have never had the nerve to do so before, invite your friends to a drag party. Admission, you tell them, will only be if they are dressed in the clothes of the opposite sex and, you inform them, after a certain time, the door of the party will be locked and no-one will be allowed in or out. This last action has the remarkable effect of making people lose their inhibitions. It's as if, because they know they cannot escape, they throw caution to the winds.

Want to make others feel different?

The remarkable Tuppy Owens, (creator of The Outsiders Club, a sex club for the disabled) writes of a fun game in her Safer Planet Sex (see appendix for details).

271 She suggests you get hold of an ordinary pair of dark glasses which you conspicuously label X-Ray Specs.

Wearing them, you then look hard at people as if you can truly see inside their body. Even though people know that this is hardly likely, there is still surprising hesitation as they fleetingly picture the dark corners of that might be under observation.

Sex trick: this is a brilliant method of beginning chat up lines.

Get back to nature

272 And if you are yearning to live a little differently try the experiment of going to a naturist resort (preferably in a hot country). The authors can recommend a trip to Cap d'Agde on the Languedoc/Roussillon coast in France. Here there is a government developed naturist resort consisting of four miles of golden beach, plus nightclubs and supermarkets, all attended by people in the nude. There are perfectly ordinary families and locals attending. There are also, if you know where to look, beach clubs and swing clubs for those who want to experiment. To find out more, look out for Loisiers magazine, which features all kinds of outdoor activities. (Loisiers, BP-3032 Nimes Cedex).

Are you an intimate lover?

273 It's all very well being daring and innovative in bed. But if you never achieve any sense of intimacy, you will never feel entirely happy.

✦ Can you talk about anything in bed?
✦ Can you look into each other's eyes as you make love?
✦ Can you make love without intercourse?
✦ Can you offer your lover sexual treats that do nothing for you?

No prizes for guessing that all 'yes's are excellent and all 'no's are not.

Five moves
to intimacy

Five further moves to intimacy

279 Show affection – small touches count.

280 Be forgiving – learn to count to 10.

281 Be amusing – try to entertain and be funny.

282 Say thank you – take nothing for granted.

283 Say sorry when you've screwed up.
As long as you can tell someone that you like, love and trust them enough to open up about your own fears, you've got a pretty good beginning.

Safer Sex

Aids

284 Unless you know that you and your woman friend could not possibly have been infected with AIDS because you are both virgins, you need to take precautions against contacting this deadly sexual disease. This means protecting yourself by using condoms, avoiding a lot of casual sex and avoiding rough sex that might break your own or your partner's skin.

AIDS stands for acquired immuno-deficiency syndrome. This literally means break-down of the immune system. You can only get it if you have contracted HIV first. HIV stands for human immuno-deficiency virus. This is caught through unprotected sex, sharing needles if you are a drug addict, and occasionally via a blood transfusion.

285 Putting on a condom. There's a right way and a wrong way and your condom application matters. That's because there is a tip on the end of each condom that must be pinched to keep the air out of it since if you put the condom on while the air remains inside it stands a good chance of popping thanks to the hearty battering it will receive.

Do not unroll your condom in advance. Holding the tip in one hand, fit the condom over the head of your penis and with the other hand roll it down in a tight fit. Only when the condom reaches the bottom of your shaft can you let go of the tip.

Sexy Books

How to Make Great Love to a Woman by Anne Hooper and Phillip Hodson (Robson Books, London, 2000).

How to Make Great Love to a Man by Phillip Hodson and Anne Hooper (Robson Books, London, 2000).

These are twin full colour manuals that detail the differences and the similarities between men and women and explains how to make the sensual most of these.

Safer Planet Sex by Tuppy Owens (Tuppy Owens) is updated and reissued every year. It is available from The Leydig Trust, P.O.Box 4ZB. London, W1A 4ZB, UK, price £8.99 UK. £10.00 Europe, US $25.00 (p & p inc).
This is a cross between a diary, an address book and a bible of sex information.

Sex Toy Tricks by Jay Wiseman (Greenery Press, San Francisco, 1996).
A briefly written but usefully specific book about every kind of sex toy imaginable. It lists where to buy them, how to use them, support groups, the lot.

Better Sex Naturally by Chris.D.Meletis,N.D. (HarperResource, New York, 2000).
Lists herbs and other natural supplements that can jumpstart your sex life. A well-informed, well-researched, intelligent collection, this investigates side effects, what specifically the herbs may do, plus the relevant scientific research.

Sex - the Good Web Guide by Matt Blythe and Jenny Blythe (The Good Web Guide, London, 2000).
An enterprising list of some of the many sex web sites to be found on the Internet. Had you heard of Eros Village? Belly Magazine? CleanSheets.com? There's a whole new world out there.

Romantic Interludes by Kenneth Ray Stubbs (Secret Garden, Larkspur, CA 1996).
The master guru of sexual massage (this includes with the tongue!) shares an incredible variation of fabulous sexual touch.

Sexy Web Sites

Sex aids
www.goodvibes.com
www.sh-womenstore.com
www.annsummers.com
www.passion8.co.uk
www.stockroom.com/sec0506.htm

Massage oils
www.momentum98.com/masoils.html
www.nealsyardremedies.com

Fabulous rubber, leather and PVC clothing
www.skintwo.com

Good sexual reading sites
www.nerve.com
www.erotica-readers.com
http://dsoft.minx.nu/main.html